ALICE'S
ADVENTUROUS
PUZZLES

ALICE'S
ADVENTUROUS
PUZZLES

Dr Gareth Moore

ARCTURUS

ARCTURUS

This edition published in 2018 by Arcturus Publishing Limited
26/27 Bickels Yard, 151–153 Bermondsey Street,
London SE1 3HA

ISBN: 978-1-78828-365-6
AD006098NT

Printed in China

Contents

Introduction 6

Puzzles 8

Solutions 222

Introduction

Lewis Carroll, the author of both *Alice's Adventures in Wonderland* and its sequel, *Through the Looking-Glass*, was a huge fan of puzzles. He created many of his own, and is often said to have invented the word ladder, a popular puzzle. He also created various cryptographic ciphers, allowing messages to be hidden in plain sight by encoding the letters in cunning ways.

Even Lewis Carroll's writing name was a puzzle. His real name was in fact Charles Lutwidge Dodgson, but he created his pen name by first translating his given names into Latin, resulting in Carolus Ludovicus. This he then translated back into English, resulting in Carol Lewis. Finally, he reversed those names to end up with his famous alter ego: Lewis Carroll.

This book is packed full of all kinds of puzzles. Some are types that Charles Dodgson would have been familiar with, such as rebus puzzles or word ladders, of course. However, many are far more modern inventions that will be new even to most contemporary readers. There is also a wide range of lateral-thinking puzzles, where you will need to use your skill and intuition to puzzle out the most likely solution to a given conundrum. Still further puzzles require you to think logically or to use your word skills. And occasionally, and only when explicitly stated, some puzzles will rely on your knowledge of the original stories.

Once you're ready to begin your journey into Wonderland, why not turn the page and accompany Alice on her latest puzzling adventures?

Time for Wonderland

One fine day, Alice was lying on the riverbank, idly picking daisies with the intention of chaining them together, when she heard a small, squeaky, and rather panicked voice.

"Oh dear!" it said. "I'm going to be late!"

Alice turned to find the source of the voice, hoping to perhaps offer some words of assurance. To her great surprise it was coming from a White Rabbit, who was hurrying past her and checking his pocket watch with what seemed to Alice to be an unnecessary frequency.

"Excuse me," she said, not altogether sure of the proper way to address a rabbit with a pocket watch.

"What is it?" the Rabbit answered irritably. "Can't you see I'm in a rush?"

"I'm sorry," replied Alice. "But I just wondered whether I might be able to help you."

The Rabbit's frown softened, or so she fancied, but it was hard to tell on a creature without eyebrows.

"As a matter of fact, you could," he replied. "Can you tell me the time? My pocket watch takes on five minutes for every hour, and I haven't reset it since 8 p.m. yesterday evening."

Alice didn't have a pocket watch of her own, but she thought she might be able to help the rabbit anyway.

"What time does your pocket watch say it is now?" she asked.

"Twelve twenty-eight," the rabbit told her.

What time did that mean it really was?

Can you answer
Alice's question?

Down the Rabbit Hole ❧

After Alice had helped the White Rabbit to ascertain the correct time, he immediately hurried off, still lamenting loudly.

"I'm going to be late! Oh, I'm going to be much too late!"

Her curiosity piqued, Alice decided to follow after the Rabbit, determined to discover where it was that a White Rabbit with a pocket watch might be trying to get to in such a hurry. She caught up with him just in time to see him disappearing into a large rabbit hole. With only a moment's hesitation, Alice went in after him.

She found herself in a maze-like warren of tunnels, with earth crumbling all around her. The Rabbit clearly knew these tunnels well, for he darted through them so quickly that he was soon out of sight.

Can you help Alice find her way through the maze of tunnels, from the top to the bottom? You'll notice that some of the tunnels have small bridges that you can walk under or where you can cross through to other tunnels, making it much more confusing than it would otherwise be.

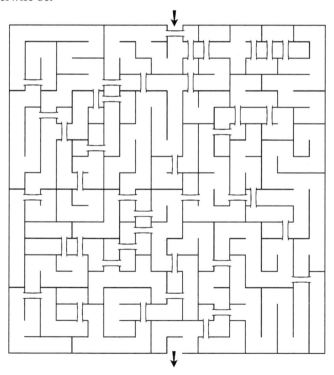

The Long Fall

Alice emerged from the maze of tunnels and, before she knew it, she noticed that she was falling into what seemed to be a very deep well. She fell and she fell and she fell, and still there was no sign of the bottom of the well. She felt strangely calm, even though she had been falling for such a long time. It didn't seem as if she was going very fast, and she thought that perhaps it wouldn't be too painful if she did eventually reach the bottom, so long as there was something soft there to break her fall: soft pillows, perhaps, or a nice pile of leaves.

After all, thought Alice, her father had once been working on the house and had fallen clean off a twenty-foot ladder. There had been nothing to break his fall, and and yet he had not been hurt at all.

What mundane explanation is there for how Alice's father had survived his fall without injury?

The Shrinking Bottle ❧

Alice eventually floated gently down to the ground, and found herself in a room without any visible exit. There was, however, a single bottle sitting right in the middle of a single table. The bottle had a label on it: DRINK ME.

Never one to lack curiosity, Alice immediately opened the bottle and smelled its contents. It didn't *smell* like it was dangerous, so she took a cautious sip. All at once, Alice had the strangest sensation. She felt she was shrinking, and indeed the ground *did* seem to be getting closer. After a moment or two, much to Alice's interest, this stopped, and when she looked around she observed that she had shrunk to two-thirds of her usual height. Intrigued, she took a second sip, and again she began to shrink, this time shrinking to two-thirds of the height she had just been.

From this new perspective, Alice was able to see a very small door at the bottom of the wall. It couldn't have been more than 5 cm high and this, she decided, must be the way out.

Given that Alice was 120 cm tall before she began to drink from the bottle, how many more sips did she need to take before she would be able to walk normally through the door without bending over?

Tweedledum and Tweedledee 1 ❧

Alice left the room and immediately came upon the White Rabbit, who welcomed her to Wonderland and gave her what he evidently considered sage advice but which seemed to Alice to be nothing but a stream of nonsense. He then scurried off behind a bush, thus vanishing from Alice's view.

Alice was minded to follow, when two identical men dressed in identical caps and identical dungarees suddenly came into view and addressed her directly.

"Hello, young lady," said the one on the left.

"And who might you be?" said the one on the right.

"For I'm Tweedledum," said the one on the left.

"And I'm Tweedledee," said the one on the right.

Alice was suddenly grateful to the White Rabbit, for he had mentioned these two. He had warned her of their mischievousness, and warned her that at least one of them always lied.

Given this information, what was the name of the man of on the left?

Too Big for Court ❧

Lots of things in Wonderland made Alice change size, but perhaps the biggest she grew was when she was at court as a witness for the trial of the Knave of Hearts. On that occasion they had tried to banish her from court for violating Rule 42: *No persons more than a mile tall are allowed in court*. But in fact, Alice wasn't quite a mile high. Rather, she was 40 feet tall plus a third of her actual height.

How tall was she?

Remembering Forward ✒

One of the strangest characters Alice came across during her travels in Wonderland was the White Queen. She lived through a looking glass, so she lived partially backward in time. This meant that she felt the effects of things before they happened, and could remember things from the future.

"Sometimes I wish I could predict the future," Alice said to her, when she found out about this strange power.

"Well, of course you can, dear," said the White Queen. "It's quite simple."

What did she mean? How could Alice predict the future without use of any magical powers?

Not Enough Tea

At a party one day, the Mad Hatter laid out nine tea cups in a surprisingly neat row. He began to pour steaming pink tea into them from an absurdly ornate and long-spouted teapot. As he filled the fourth cup, however, the stream of tea reduced to a dribble, and it became clear that the pot was empty.

"The tea's run out," said the March Hare.

"It's stopped running out," said the Hatter.

"I think he means there isn't any left," said Alice.

"Yes there is," said the Hatter. "It's in the cups."

"But there isn't enough for the rest of the cups," Alice said.

"True," said the Hatter. "It's lucky there are only three of us."

A miserable squeak came from the teapot.

"Four of us," the March Hare corrected.

"True," said the Hatter. "Now here's a challenge for you, Alice. At the moment, all four filled teacups are at one end of the row, with five empty ones next to them. Can you make them alternate between filled and not filled. But here's the catch: You can move only two of the cups."

How could it be done?

Not Enough Cake ~

Alice once again came across the White Rabbit, who was looking very upset.

"My dear rabbit! Whatever is wrong?" she asked.

"Why, but I have just been to the Mad Hatter's Tea Party," he sniffled. "They had an enormous carrot cake, which is the kind I like the most. But the Hatter himself took half the slices plus two more, and then the March Hare took half the remaining slices plus two more, and then the Dormouse took half the remaining slices plus two more, and then there wasn't any left for me!"

If this was so, how many slices of cake were there to start with?

Three Bottles ❧

One day, the residents of Wonderland presented Alice with three potion bottles of three different sizes. One was made by the Caterpillar and contained mushroom potion. One was made by the White Rabbit and contained carrot potion. One was made by the Cook and contained pepper potion.

Alice was told that one of the potions would make her shrink, one would make her grow, and one would have no effect on her size. She was also told the following:

- She would end up bigger if she drank from the carrot potion than she would if she drank from the biggest bottle.
- She would end up smaller if she drank from the smallest bottle than she would if she drank from the pepper potion.
- The White Rabbit's potion was not in the smallest bottle.

Based on this information, can you deduce which potion was in which bottle, and how each potion would affect Alice's size?

In The Kitchen ❧

One day Alice found herself in the Duchess's kitchen, helping the Cook to prepare a meal. On a high shelf there was a basket marked POTATOES, a basket marked CARROTS, and a basket marked POTATOES AND CARROTS.

"The Duchess's baby changed the labels," the Cook warned her, "and now they're all wrong. Could you pass me five carrots?"

Alice could only just reach into the baskets, and they were far too heavy to move. What is the fewest number of vegetables Alice needs to reach for in order to work out which basket is which?

The Right Size

Alice came across a door with two locks that were very far apart. She calculated that in order to be able to reach both at the same time, she would need to be exactly 19 cm taller than she currently was. Moreover, she had a potion that made her shrink with each sip, and a cake that made her grow with each bite. The potion made her shrink by 3 cm, and the cake made her grow by 8 cm.

What was the minimum total number of sips and bites she needed to consume in order to reach her precise desired height?

The Head Start 🐾

The Mad Hatter and the March Hare decided to have a race. They carefully measured out a course of 100 m, using hats to mark the start and finish. They had Alice stand at the finish line in case it was a close call. But, as it turned out, the March Hare won the race by 10 m.

"I want a rematch!" said the Hatter to the Hare. "And as you're faster, you should start further back!"

The Hare agreed that this seemed fair. Since he had won by 10 m, they started him 10 m before the original start line.

Assuming both the Hatter and the Hare ran at the same speed they had in the previous race, who would win in this new arrangement?

The Not Lemonade ✎

Alice was helping the Cook in the Duchess's kitchen. It was a hot day, so when they had finished cooking the Cook poured them some lemonade on ice. The Duchess drank hers almost immediately, but the slightly peppery taste made Alice rather struggle with hers, particularly because she kept sneezing between every sip.

She eventually managed to finish the whole glass, but as she made to stand up she discovered she had shrunk down to the size of a large cat. The Cook, however, had been completely unaffected by her drink.

Given that they were drinking the same thing, and both would react to Wonderland magic in the same way, can you find something that could explain why Alice shrank but the cook did not?

Cake Selection ᔆ

"What types of cake do you have?" Alice asked the Mad Hatter one day.

"Well, that is an easy question, with an easy answer: All but two of them are carrot cakes, all but two of them are jam sponges, and all but two of them are coffee cakes," he told her.

How many cakes did the Mad Hatter have in total?

The Sentence

"Off with his head!" said the Red Queen, when the Knave of Hearts was found guilty of a crime. But the Knave pleaded for a different sentence, and so the Queen came up with some alternatives.

She said, "Your choices are as follows: you may be beheaded, set on fire, or locked in a room with a Bandersnatch that hasn't eaten in two months."

What should the Knave have chosen?

Tweedledum and Tweedledee 2 ✿

After their first run-in, when both Tweedledum and Tweedledee had lied to Alice about their names, she had managed to convince Tweedledum of the value of honesty, and persuaded him to start telling the truth. Tweedledee, however, remained resolute in his resolve to lie about everything. The trouble was that with the two brothers being so very identical, Alice could never tell which of them was which, and as a result she never knew whether the brother she was addressing was speaking truthfully or not.

"Are you Tweedledum?" she asked one of them, upon coming across them in a clearing.

"If I am Tweedledum," he said, "then my brother is Tweedledee."

Did this answer help Alice to determine which brother she was speaking to?

Too Many Queens ❧

Have you seen the White Queen?" Alice asked the Cheshire Cat.

"Queens," said the Cheshire Cat. "They move very fast on a chessboard, you know."

"They move along rows, columns, or diagonals, and can move any number of squares" said Alice. "I know."

"But here's an interesting question. How many queens could you place on an 8×8 chessboard without any of them being able to attack another on their first move?"

Shifting Words 1 ❧

The Mad Hatter has shifted the letters of the following Lewis Carroll quotation five places forward alphabetically.

Can you shift them back to reveal the question?

Bmd nx f wfajs qnpj f bwnynsl-ijxp?

Tea Party Invitations ❧

"I'm inviting people for tea," said the Mad Hatter. "Alice, would you give out these invitations?"

Alice looked at the names on the envelopes. "I don't understand," she said. "Who are all these people?"

"Oh yes, I haven't written their names in the usual way," he explained. "I think letters must get so tired of being in the same order all the time, so I've jumbled them up. I'm sure you can work them out though, my dear."

Alice looked at the envelopes again. The names were as follows:
- Hectic Share
- A Frequent Shoe
- Bib With Tear
- Freaks Have Not
- Mutter Lock

Can you unscramble the names and work out who the Mad Hatter had invited?

Down the Stairs ॐ

There was a single staircase in the Duchess's house. When Alice went inside and began to grow, she was able to climb the steps of the staircase five steps at a time, leaving her with three steps to hop up at the top. Once she had shrunk back down she could only jump down three steps at a time, leaving her with two steps to hop down right at the bottom.

What is the smallest number of steps there could have been in the staircase?

Magic Mushrooms ❧

The Caterpillar gave Alice three baskets, each of which contained two mushrooms. One basket was marked TWO FOR GROWING, one was marked TWO FOR SHRINKING, and the third was marked ONE FOR GROWING AND ONE FOR SHRINKING.

"Of course," the Caterpillar told her, "it would be dreadfully dull if the baskets were correctly marked. Thus I have mixed up the labels so that each basket has the wrong label."

Alice would not have been opposed to the dreadfully dull state of affairs in which all baskets were correctly marked, but she decided not to argue. Instead, she thanked the Caterpillar and headed on her way. As she walked, she found herself beginning to shrink. The more she shrank, the slower she became, and she decided that it was worth trying to eat one of the mushrooms the Caterpillar had given her in the hope that it might reverse her shrinking.

From which basket should she take a mushroom to maximize her chances of getting a growing mushroom?

A Pie Problem

Alice was packing away pies in the Duchess's kitchen. The Cook had given Alice sixteen pies and four boxes of different sizes in which to pack them.

"I want four pies in each box," she told Alice. "No more and no less."

Alice had set out the four boxes on the table, and had just managed to squeeze four pies into each box when the White Rabbit came charging into the kitchen.

"Have you seen the Duchess's gloves?" he asked. "Oh dear, oh dear, I'm going to be late, and I can't find the gloves!"

As he did a frantic circuit of the kitchen, he collided with the table, knocking two boxes of pies onto the floor. Alice retrieved the boxes, but to her dismay the pies inside had broken and she had to throw them away.

"Look what you've done!" she said to the rabbit, which only made him more distressed. "Now I can't put four pies into each box!"

"Oh dear, oh dear," he said, throwing her a concerned look, and then hurried away.

Alice sat down and looked at the boxes of pies and felt tears starting in her eyes. She didn't want to make the Cook angry again, but she didn't see what she could do. Then, however, a solution occurred to her.

How was Alice able to pack the eight remaining pies so that each of the four boxes contained exactly four pies?

The Hand that was Dealt ✒

The Mad Hatter, the March Hare, and the Dormouse were each holding a single playing card. One of these cards was a two, one was a seven, and one was a queen. One was a club, one was a diamond, and one was a heart.

Alice also knew the following:
- The Hare's card was higher than the diamond.
- The seven's suit was earlier in the alphabet than the Dormouse's suit.
- The queen was not the queen of hearts.

Can you deduce which card each of the three held?

Shifting Words 2 ～

The Mad Hatter has shifted backward the letters of the following Lewis Carroll quotation by a certain number of places alphabetically. Can you work out the shift and reveal the quotation?

Gd wms bml'r ilmu ufcpc wms ypc emgle,
ylw pmyb ayl ryic wms rfcpc.

Tweedledum and Tweedledee 3 🐝

The next time Alice came across Tweedledum and Tweedledee, they were talking to a little dormouse.

"I'd never steal a piece of cheese," said the Dormouse. "So let me go now, if you please!"

"Does he lie or tell the truth?" Alice asked the brothers.

"He always lies," said one of the brothers.

"He sometimes lies," said the other brother.

So does the Dormouse lie, tell the truth, or both?

Strange Sequences 1 ❧

While sitting atop his mushroom and smoking merrily, the Caterpillar's latest habit is to pose passers-by a continue-the-sequence question. By way of incentive to partake in his game, he gives a piece of a magical mushroom to the passer-by who is able to provide the correct next letter.

Can you identify which letter should come next in the following timely sequence?

YYHLYEY _

The Three Pieces

Alice was once told about three chess pieces on a board: a bishop, a pawn, and a rook. Numbering the chess board columns from A to H, and the rows from 1 to 8, one piece was in column A, one in column B, and one in column E. One piece was in row 3, one in row 4, and one in row 7.

Alice also knew the following:
- The pawn was in a higher row number than the piece in column B.
- The piece in row four was in an earlier column letter than the bishop.
- The piece in row 4 moved three times as many squares in its previous turn as the piece in column A.

Can you deduce which piece was in which square of the board?

Looking Through the Looking Glass ❧

One day, before making her way through the looking glass, Alice had peered into it and was surprised to see a collection of books on a shelf with their names written in a strange tongue. She guessed that it must be the language of Wonderland. Among the titles she saw were:

- *Dribgnik Comal Likot*, by Eel Reprah
- *Eyreh Tnireh Ctaceht*, by Regnilas Dj
- *Ekaws Nagen Nif*, by Ecyoj Semaj
- *Dnalred Nowni Serutnev Dasecila*, by Llorrac Siwel

Can you translate these titles into English?

Strange Sequences 2 ❧

Still sitting atop his mushroom and smoking merrily, the Caterpillar continues his habit of posing passers-by a continue-the-sequence question. By way of incentive to partake in his game, he gives a piece of a magical mushroom to the passer-by who is able to provide the correct next letter.

Can you identify which letter should come next in the following sequence?

W T F S S M _

Shifting Words 3 ❧

The Mad Hatter has shifted forward the letters of the following Lewis Carroll quotation by a certain number of places alphabetically. Can you deduce the shift and identify the quotation?

Q svme epw Q eia bpqa uwzvqvo, jcb Q'dm kpivoml i nme bquma aqvkm bpmv.

Hidden Figures ☙

A Wonderland character is hiding within each of these sentences. Can you find them all?

- It was during the original ice age.

- Taekwondo doesn't require much equipment.

- I made an angry phone call.

- The plan for renewal rushed us.

- I found that terrifying.

Character Match-up

Can you match up the words in the left and right columns to make the names of eight Wonderland residents?

CHESHIRE	BIRD
HUMPTY	CAT
FROG	DUMPTY
JUBJUB	FOOTMAN
MAD	HARE
MARCH	HATTER
MOCK	KING
RED	RABBIT
WHITE	TURTLE

Too Many Legs ❧

When Alice first arrived in Wonderland, she came across a large group of animals. Most of them were birds of different sorts, and the rest were mice. The birds all had two legs, as birds so often do, and the mice all had four, again the most common arrangement.

Alice counted that all together the birds and mice had 26 heads and 64 legs.

Can you work out how many birds and how many mice there were?

Stolen Vowels 1 ❧

The Knave of Hearts has stolen all of the vowels and spaces from these Wonderland residents.

Can you restore them all?

CTRPLLR

DRMS

MDHTTR

RDKNG

WHTRBBT

Strange Sequences 3 ❧

Still sitting atop his mushroom and smoking merrily, the Caterpillar continues his habit of posing passers-by a continue-the-sequence question. By way of incentive to partake in his game, he gives a piece of a magical mushroom to the passer-by who is able to provide the correct next letter.

Can you identify which letter should come next in the following sequence of last letters?

D E W N E O _

Strange Sequences 4 ❧

The Caterpillar then sets a teaser which he is sure will prove a challenge to even the most intelligent of passers-by.

Can you solve it by identifying which letter should come next in the following sequence?

H H L B B C N O _

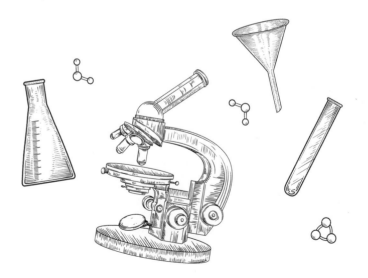

Stolen Vowels 2 ❧

The Knave of Hearts has stolen all of the vowels and spaces from these Wonderland residents.

Can you restore them all?

BNDRSNTCH

CHSHRCT

MCKTRTL

MRCHHR

TWDLDM

Split Titles 1

The titles of six chapters of *Alice's Adventures in Wonderland* have each been split into two groups of alternating letters. Can you reunite each group from the left with its pair on the right?

A_A_T_A_A_T_   _D_I_E_R_M_C_T_R_I_L_R

A_V_C_F_O_A_A_E_P_L_A_   _H_M_C_T_R_L_S_T_R_

L_B_T_R_U_D_I_L_   _H_Q_E_N_C_O_U_T_R_U_D

T_E_A_B_T_E_D_A_I_T_E_I_L   _H_R_B_I_S_N_S_L_T_L_B_L_

T_E_O_K_U_T_E_S_O_Y   _M_D_E_P_R_Y

T_E_U_E_S_R_Q_E_G_O_N_   _O_S_E_Q_A_R_L_E

Wonderful Words

Can you join these words into pairs with a Carrollian theme? One word is the odd one out, since it pairs with itself.

- A
- Ah
- Arts
- Cater
- Corn
- Do
- Foot
- He
- Hook
- Land
- Lice
- Man
- Mush
- Pillar
- Room
- Wonder
- Uni

Split Titles 2

The titles of six chapters of *Alice's Adventures in Wonderland* have each been split into two groups of alternating letters. Can you reunite each group from the left with its pair on the right?

A_I_E_E_I_E_C_   _H_C_U_U_R_C_A_D_L_N_T_L_

D_W_T_E_A_B_T_O_E   _H_P_O_O_T_A_S

P_G_N_P_P_E_   _I_A_D_E_P_R

T_E_A_C_S_A_E_N_A_O_G_A_E   _H_S_O_E_H_T_R_S

T_E_O_L_F_E_R_   _L_C_S_V_D_N_E

W_O_T_L_T_E_A_T_   _O_N_H_R_B_I_H_L_

Strange Sequences 5 ～

Still sitting atop his mushroom and smoking merrily, the Caterpillar continues his habit of posing passers-by a continue-the-sequence question. By way of incentive to partake in his game, he gives a piece of a magical mushroom to the passer-by who is able to provide the correct next letter.

Can you identify which letter should come next in the following secondary ordering?

OTTFFSS _

Tweedledum
and Tweedledee 4 ~

On one occasion, Alice brought Tweedledum and Tweedledee to the Mad Hatter's tea party. There was a great selection of food, including three types of cake: chocolate cakes, jam sponges, and currant cakes. The brothers set about eating as many of these little cakes as they could.

"Which of the cakes is the nicest?" Alice asked them.

"Either the chocolate cakes are not the worst, or the jam sponges are the best," said one brother.

"The chocolate cakes are not the worst," said the other brother.

Assuming the two brothers agreed on how nice the cakes were, can you use their statements to rank the cakes from best to worst?

An Abundance of Tea ❧

The Mad Hatter's table was overcrowded with teacups. He explained to Alice that a month ago he had decided that, starting with one cup on the first day, he was going to pour one more cup of tea every day than he had the previous day.

On which day of this exercise did the Hatter pour his 150th cup of tea?

In Other Words ❧

Can you identify these Wonderland characters from synonyms of their names?

- The loopy milliner

- The parade leveret

- The ridicule reptile

- The college cereal seeds

- The feline um column

Changing Sizes ✒

This morning, afternoon and evening, Alice has been three different heights: 50 cm tall, 150 cm tall, and 300 cm tall. One of these heights was caused by her eating a mushroom, one by her eating a cake, and one by her drinking a potion.

Alice remembers the following:
  • Eating the mushroom made her taller than she was during the afternoon.
  • She ate the cake before she consumed whatever made her 150 cm tall.
  • The cake made her grow.

Can you deduce what she consumed at which time of day, and how tall it made her?

The Wrong Names

The Duchess was having a party. There were fifteen guests, none of whom Alice had met before. She asked the Duchess's Cook what their names were, and the Cook gave her a list of fifteen names but did not tell her which name belonged to whom. Not wanting her lists of names to go to waste, Alice decided to randomly assign each name to a guest, and used these names to address them. Over the course of the party, only one guest complained about her using the wrong name, although she didn't get to talk to everyone.

"How good my guessing was!" she thought afterward. "To have only upset one person! I wonder if I guessed all the other names correctly?"

What was the probability that Alice had guessed exactly fourteen of the names correctly?

Birds of a Feather 🐦

Alice awoke from a dream to find herself surrounded by a large circle of birds. She recognized the Dodo, the Lory, and the Eaglet, but there were many more that she'd never seen before. Starting from the Dodo, she counted the birds in the circle, noting that the 11th bird was directly opposite the 24th bird.

Assuming the birds were evenly spaced around the circle, how many birds were there in total?

A Sponge Shared ❧

Tweedledum and Tweedledee together eat a sponge cake made by the Duchess's Cook. It takes them 20 minutes. If Tweedledum had eaten the cake on his own, it would have taken him 30 minutes.

Assuming each brother has a constant rate of eating, how long would it have taken Tweedledee to eat the cake on his own?

Madness and Nonsense 🍃

"Everyone here is at least a little bit mad," said the Cheshire Cat.

"Is madness something you can have different amounts of?" asked Alice. "I thought you either were mad or you weren't."

"Don't be ridiculous," said the Cheshire Cat. "There are all kinds of madness. Why, 70 percent of people in Wonderland are less mad than average."

"That's nonsense," said Alice. "Averages don't work that way!"

Was it nonsense, or could the Cheshire Cat be right?

Shifting Words 4 ✎

The Mad Hatter has shifted backward the letters of the following Lewis Carroll quotation by a certain number of places alphabetically. Can you identify the shift and reveal the quotation?

Lwn, hdbtixbth X'kt qtaxtkts ph bpcn ph hxm xbedhhxqat iwxcvh qtudgt qgtpzuphi.

Too Big for the Kitchen

Alice must have eaten something strange in the Duchess's kitchen, because she was soon growing and growing. In fact, she was doubling in size every minute. By 12:15 she had filled half the kitchen!

At what time would she fill the whole kitchen?

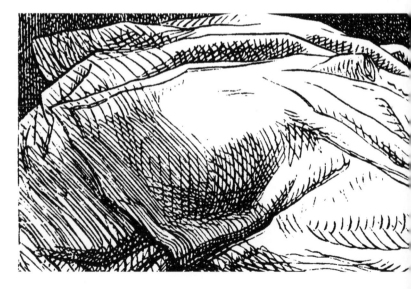

Before the Trial 🍂

The trial of the Knave of Hearts was a very hectic affair. Before it began, everyone, from the witnesses to the spectators to the accused, shook hands with everyone else exactly once. Alice calculated that this meant there were 78 handshakes in total.

How many people were at the trial?

Collecting Mushrooms ❧

The Caterpillar had asked Alice to pick 60 mushrooms by dinnertime. She worked out that if she picked mushrooms at a rate of 10 mushrooms an hour, she would manage it just in time. But it turned out to be more difficult than she expected, and she managed to collect the first half of the mushrooms at a rate of only 5 mushrooms an hour.

If she upped her rate to 15 mushrooms an hour for the remaining mushrooms, would she still manage to collect all 60 in time?

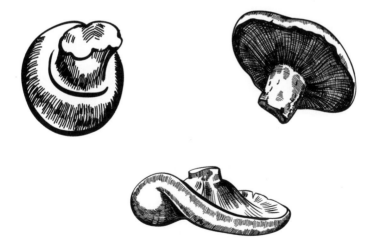

Tweedledum and Tweedledee 5 ❧

Alice was on her way to the Royal Garden, where she had been summoned to play croquet with the Queen. While she was following the directions she had been given, she arrived at a fork in the road. She couldn't remember if she was meant to go left or right, or if she'd even been told about the fork at all. She thought and she thought, but nothing came to her, so she sat down where she was and soon felt herself on the verge of tears.

"Is it losing your way that's made you frown?" said a voice.

"Or did you need some sitting down?" said another.

Alice looked up to discover that Tweedledum and Tweedledee were approaching her from the left-hand path in front of her.

"Oh!" she said. "Maybe you can help me! Is that the way to the Royal Garden?"

"It is," replied one of the brothers.

"It isn't," said the other.

"Oh, this is useless," said Alice. "If I don't know which of you is which, you can't help me at all!"

But then she thought of a way to ask her question which would get her the right answer, regardless of whether she was talking to Tweedledum or Tweedledee.

What was it?

Plates of Cakes

The Mad Hatter was distributing cakes onto plates around the table. He put one on the first plate, and then on each subsequent plate he put more cakes than he had on the previous one. Once he'd gone all the way around the table, he'd put down 80 cakes in total.

What is the maximum number of plates there could have been around the table?

Talking Flowers ❧

When Alice first went through the looking-glass, she happened across a vase of flowers that could talk. She was startled at first, but she was quite used to strange things happening, and it soon seemed perfectly natural to her that flowers should talk, and perfectly odd that she'd never heard them talking before.

There were three flowers that she spoke to the most: a rose, a daisy, and a tiger-lily. One of them was white, one was pink, and the third red. Alice also observed that:

- The tiger-lily was taller than the white flower.
- The flower of medium height had a shorter name than the pink flower.
- The pink flower was not the tallest.

Can you deduce which flower was pink, which was red, and which was white, and how tall they were in relation to one another?

Sense and Nonsense ❧

The first sentence of *Alice's Adventures in Wonderland* has been manipulated by altering the vowels. Can you work out how it has been altered, and reveal the original opening sentence?

Eloci wes bigonnong tu git viry torid uf sottong by hir sostir un thi benk, end uf hevong nothong tu du.

Something Forgotten ❧

Alice was wandering around in the woods, with the vague sense that she had forgotten something very important, except that she really couldn't think what it was. She shortly came upon a Fawn with big gentle eyes, who did not look at all troubled to see her.

"Excuse me," she said, "but I wonder if you could help me. You see, I think I've forgotten something, but I'm not sure what it is."

"You have," said the Fawn. "You've forgotten something that belongs to you."

Alice pondered for a moment whether she could have forgotten something that *didn't* belong to her, and she supposed that she could have.

"The curious thing," said the Fawn, "is that although what you've forgotten belongs to you, you don't use it all that much. In fact, other people use it a lot more than you do."

What had Alice forgotten?

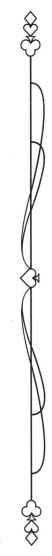

Nonsensical Numbers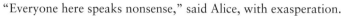

"Everyone here speaks nonsense," said Alice, with exasperation.

"That's nonsense," said Tweedledum.

"Just because you don't understand it, that doesn't mean it's nonsense," said Tweedledee.

Alice didn't like being accused of not understanding things. "Are you telling me that someone could say 'ten plus seven equals five' and not be speaking nonsense?"

"Sometimes ten plus seven does equal five," said Tweedledum.

"It all depends on what you are doing," said Tweedledee.

So, when does ten plus seven equal five?

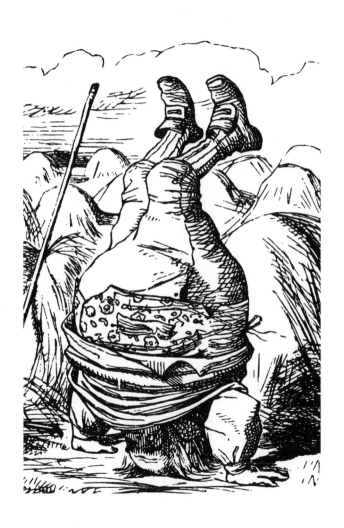

Doubling on the Chessboard ❧

"How much would you charge for a single tomato seed?" the Red Queen asked the White Queen.

"A single seed?" asked the White Queen. "Why, only a single pence."

"I will give you a trillion pounds, then," said the Red Queen, "to plant one tomato seed on the first square of the chessboard, two on the second square, four on the third, eight on the fourth, and so on, doubling every square, right up until you have planted the correct number of seeds on the 64th square."

Should the White Queen accept this deal?

Too Many Bishops ❧

Throughout her travels in Wonderland, Alice met many chess pieces, but she never did meet a bishop. She remarked on this to Tweedledum and Tweedledee.

"Yes, well they move in diagonals," said Tweedledum, "so it's easy to miss them."

"Not to mention, they're very antisocial," said Tweedledee.

"Here's a question," said Tweedledum. "How many bishops could you place on a chessboard, so that none of them shared a diagonal, and none of them were in adjacent squares?"

The Dinner Conundrum ~

One day, Alice was invited to tea, and there were nameplates to show clearly in which place each person was to sit. However, the names had been written in somewhat whimsical ways.

One of the nameplates read:

A. Nits

Who was intended to sit at this seat?

More Sense and Nonsense

The first sentence of *Through the Looking-Glass* has been encoded by altering every other letter. Can you work out how it has been altered, and reveal the original opening sentence?

Ome shhnf wzs beqtzim, tgas tge vhhtd khtsem hzd gac nntgimg so co vish ht—ht var tge alzcj khtsem's eatls emthrdlx.

Tweedledum and Tweedledee 6 🐌

Alice came upon a great river, and was looking for a way to cross it. She saw a small, wooden rowing boat tied to a tree a little way downstream from her and went over to it, planning to untie it and use it to cross the river.

"Excuse me," said a voice, as she was fumbling with the rope, "but that's my boat!"

She turned to discover that either Tweedledum or Tweedledee was standing behind her, and looking rather cross.

That might be Tweedledee instead of Tweedledum, she thought to herself, in which case it's not his boat at all. But I suppose I can't be sure, and either way, he looks as if he'd be angry if I took it.

"May I borrow it?" she asked, hoping his answer might give her a clue as to which of the brothers he was.

"You may borrow it if and only if my name is Tweedledum," he replied.

So should Alice continue trying to untie the boat?

110

Mathematical Mushroom 1 🐦

Can you fill the boxes in this mathematical mushroom with numbers from the range 1 to 9? Each connected number adds together to make the total given at the end of that line, and no number can be repeated within a line.

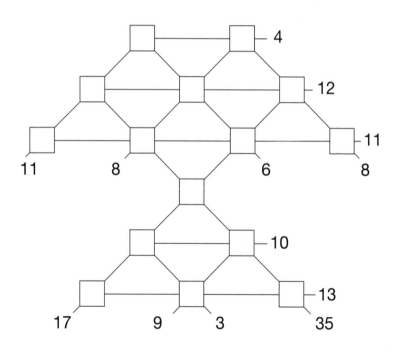

Back to Square One ❧

"How many squares are there on a chessboard?" asked the Red Queen. "That's easy," said Alice, who had learned how to work this kind of thing out at school. "There are eight rows and eight columns, and eight times eight is sixty-four."

"There are sixty-four squares that are one square big, yes, but what about all the larger squares?"

"Larger squares?" asked Alice, perplexed.

"Yes," said the Red Queen. "Squares made up of four little squares, or nine little squares, or sixteen little squares, and so on."

"Oh, I see," said Alice. But even though she understood the question, she had no idea how to go about answering it.

What is the answer?

Broken Chessboard 🐦

This chessboard is broken! Can you fit the pieces back together to make an 8×8 chessboard, in which the squares alternate between black and white? The pieces are in the correct orientation, so they don't need to be rotated.

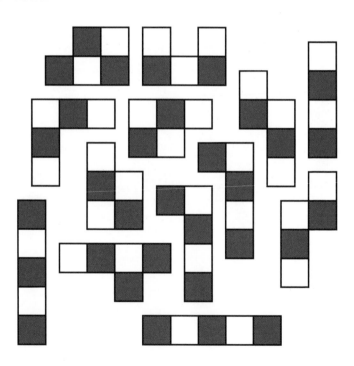

Chess and Dominoes

Tweedledum and Tweedledee were playing chess, and they asked Alice if she wanted to join them.

"I'm sick and tired of chess!" she said. "Everything in this world is about chess. I don't know how you can play any more of it!"

"We also have dominoes," said Tweedledum. "We could play that instead."

"No, thank you," said Alice. "I really don't feel like playing any sort of game at the moment."

As she was talking to Tweedledum, Tweedledee had been laying out the dominoes on the chessboard, so that each domino covered exactly two squares of the board. He was able to place 32 dominoes, so that every square of the board was covered.

"That's no challenge," said Tweedledum, looking over at it. He shook the dominoes off the board, retrieved a large pair of scissors from his pocket, and then cut off two opposite corner squares of the board. "Now see if you can cover all the squares with 31 dominoes."

Could it be done?

The Mad Hatter has shifted forward the letters of the following Lewis Carroll quotation by a certain number of places alphabetically. Can you deduce the shift and identify the quotation?

Osgmotgzout oy znk utre ckgvut ot znk cgx gmgotyz xkgroze.

Card Tricks

Alice had been wandering around in the Royal Gardens when she came upon the Royal Gardeners: the Two of Hearts, the Five of Hearts, and the Seven of Hearts. She struck up a conversation with them, and the Five of Hearts asked if she would like to see a card trick. She agreed, half expecting the trick to involve the three gardeners themselves, but in fact he had with him his own small pack of cards. He handed a pile of them to Alice.

"Rotate one of the cards and then put it back in the pack," he said.

Alice looked through the cards. She saw a total of seven hearts, seven clubs, and seven spades. For each of these suits, she had the ace, three, five, six, seven, eight, and nine. There were also two diamonds: the three of diamonds and the seven of diamonds. She turned round the three of diamonds and then handed the stack back to the gardener. He looked through them quickly.

"You chose the three of diamonds!" he said triumphantly.

"But I made sure the card would look identical when rotated, and it did!" exclaimed Alice, confused as to how he had successfully identified her card.

How did the trick work, and why did he give Alice that particular selection of cards?

Card Watching ❧

"The Queen of Hearts is looking for you," the Cheshire Cat told Alice, "with all of her eyes."

"All of her eyes?" Alice asked. "Doesn't she just have two?"

"Oh, but have you never seen a deck of cards before?" the Cheshire Cat enquired enigmatically.

"Of course I have!" said Alice indignantly.

"Then you ought to know as well as anyone that there are four eyes on the Queen of Hearts."

Alice considered this. She was sure each of the Queen's faces had two eyes, but then she remembered that there were two faces on each face card.

"I see what you mean," she replied.

"But here's something you probably haven't considered before. How many eyes are visible in a standard pack of cards?"

House of Cards ✎

Alice was daydreaming about building a giant house of cards from some of the playing cards in Wonderland. She had tried building a house of cards before, with a pack of cards her sister had given her. The first layer had had 6 cards in it, leaning against each other in pairs. Then there were 2 cards placed flat across the tops. Above that were 4 more cards, also leaning against each other in pairs, with 1 card placed flat across them, and then a final pair leaning against each other at the top. Alice's tower looked like this:

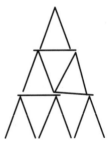

She had started again on a larger house of cards, but Dinah came in and knocked it all over, and she didn't have the heart to start again.

Building a house of cards in the same way that Alice once did, what is the maximum number of layers you can make if you start with a standard 52-card deck, so that it starts with an upright layer and finishes with an upright pair at the top? Count both upright and flat layers in the total layer count.

Blind Man's Bluff

Tweedledum had blindfolded Tweedledee, and then handed him a pack of cards in which, he explained, 16 were face up and the other 36 were face down.

"Sort these into two piles," he said, "so that each pile has the same number of face-up cards."

Tweedledee thought for several minutes, and then came up with a solution. How did he do it, without being able to see any of the cards?

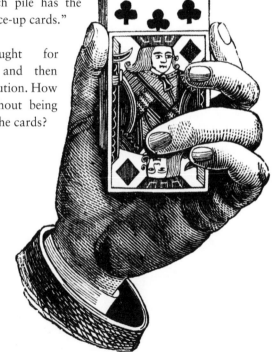

Four of a Kind ❧

Tweedledum and Tweedledee each had a standard pack of 52 cards. They put both packs together into one larger pile between them, and both began drawing vast quantities of cards until finally Tweedledum said, "Bingo!"

He showed Tweedledee that he had four twos.

What's the lowest number of cards Tweedledum would have had to draw from the two packs to guarantee that he got four of a kind?

Even More Sense and Nonsense ❧

A passage from *Through the Looking-Glass* has been encoded by swapping pairs of letters according to a particular rule. Can you work out how it has been altered, and reveal the original passage?

Mld, sviv, blf hvv, rg gzpvh zoo gsv ifmmrmt blf xzm wl, gl pvvk rm gsv hznv kozxv. Ru blf dzmg gl tvg hlnvdsviv vohv, blf nfhg ifm zg ovzhg gdrxv zh uzhg zh gszg!

Rebus 1

Can you identify the Carrollian phrase clued by the following?

~~POSSIBLE~~

~~POSSIBLE~~

~~POSSIBLE~~

~~POSSIBLE~~

~~POSSIBLE~~

~~POSSIBLE~~

THINGS

FAST

Mad Multiplication ❧

"How many people are there in Wonderland?" Alice asked the Cheshire Cat. "I'm sure I see at least one new person every ten minutes."

"People?" asked the Cheshire Cat. "We're not all people, you know. In fact, most of us aren't."

The Cheshire Cat looked rather offended, so Alice quickly apologized. "I'm terribly sorry," said Alice. "I didn't mean anything by it. I just wondered how many animals and, um, things lived in Wonderland."

The Cat harrumphed. "Fine. I shall forgive you if you are able to answer a simple question: What would you get if you multiplied together in one giant multiplication the number of hands that each Wonderland resident has?"

Alice frowned. "But you haven't told me how many residents there are! How could I possibly work that out?"

The Cat shook his head. "Alas. It would seem you are guilty of repeating your previous mistake."

What was the answer?

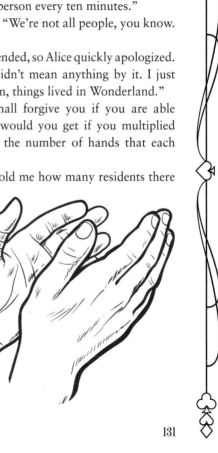

Wonderland Zigzag 1 🍂

Can you fill in the gaps in the following zigzag puzzle, which starts and ends with a Wonderland-themed word? The last two letters of each word must be the same as the first two of the next one.

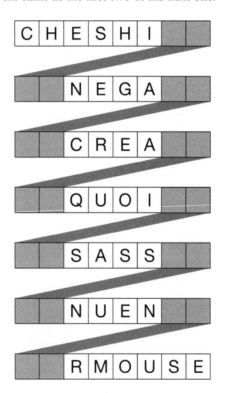

Nonsense Pairs

Can you delete one letter in each of the following letter pairs to reveal the names of some Wonderland characters?

QA BU HE KE IN OR UF SH ME AO RL ET SP

RM EA DI RH AB OT IT EC RS

CA EL IN MC EL

ML AO RA VC HI NH EA RT ES

NT UW EM RE DR LI EA VD EX ME

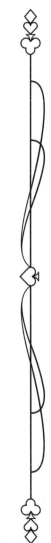

Letter Soup ✎

The names of three Wonderland characters are jumbled up in this letter soup. Can you identify them?

Muddled Testimonies ❧

There were three witnesses at the trial of the Knave of Hearts: the March Hare, the White Rabbit, and Bill the Lizard. The trouble was that the trial was very badly organized, so all three witnesses kept talking over each other, and it was very hard to work out who was saying what.

Each witness claimed to have seen the Knave of Hearts on the day of the crime: only one of them claimed to have seen him eating the tarts, one of the others had seen him sleeping, and one had seen him reading a book. One of them had seen him in the royal gardens, one had seen him in the Duchess's kitchen, and one had seen him standing beneath a giant mushroom. And one of them had seen him at 9 a.m., one at 2 p.m., and one at 7 p.m.

Alice was also able to make out the following:
- Bill the Lizard had seen the Knave of Hearts before he was at the giant mushroom.
- The Knave of Hearts was reading a book in the afternoon.
- The Knave of Hearts was sleeping in the Duchess's kitchen.
- The March Hare saw him after he'd been to the royal gardens.
- The White Rabbit saw him five hours before he ate the tarts.
- The Knave of Hearts did not eat the tarts in the royal gardens.

Based on this information, can you deduce who saw the Knave of Hearts doing what, where and when?

The Road to the Palace ~

Alice was on her way to the palace to play croquet with the Queen of Hearts. As she was walking, she saw a very strange party approaching her. As they got nearer, she saw that it was led by the Cheshire Cat. With him were six people, among whom she recognized the Duchess and the Hatter. Each of these people had with them six birds, and each bird was carrying six mice. When she got really close, she could see that each mouse was carrying six insects.

"How odd," Alice thought, though she was not nearly as surprised as she would have been if she had only just arrived in Wonderland and had not become quite accustomed to seeing strange sights such as these.

In total, counting every living being mentioned, how many were going to the palace?

The Giant Puppy ～

Alice thought that she must at that moment be very small. Alternatively, the puppy she was looking at was much, much bigger than even any fully grown dog she'd ever seen. Despite this, it didn't look too dangerous: it sat watching her with wide brown eyes and then began reaching its paw out toward her. She had half a mind to start playing with it, but the other half of her mind was slightly afraid that it might trample her, or even eat her if it was hungry. So she decided it would be best to make an escape.

She picked up a stick, which sent the puppy quite mad with excitement, and it lurched terrifyingly toward her. In a great hurry, she leaned back and threw the stick into the nearby woods with all her might, and the puppy went charging off after it.

She turned in relief and began to walk away when all of a sudden a large grin materialized beside her, and shortly after it the rest of the Cheshire Cat chose to join it.

"A good throw," he observed. "I should say that you had that puppy running as far into the woods as it was possible to go."

"And how far is that?" Alice asked. She thought that if it really had been a long throw, she might report it back to her sister.

The Cheshire Cat grinned. "You tell me. What's the farthest it's possible to go into the woods?"

Rebus 2

Can you identify the Carrollian phrase clued by the following?

THE G-GLALOOKSS

A Slow Race ❧

The Hatter was trying to teach Tweedledum and Tweedledee some patience. They were both planning to come to the tea party that day, and he told them that the brother whose trousers were the last to touch their seat would get the most cakes.

Knowing this, the brothers wandered very slowly in the direction of the tea party; so slowly, in fact, that they were hardly moving. Alice came upon them shuffling forward in this strange way and asked them what was going on. They explained their predicament to her, and she made a suggestion that soon had them racing to get to the tea party.

What did Alice suggest?

Lewis Carroll's Bookshelf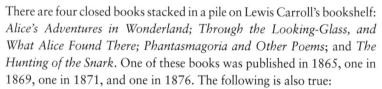

There are four closed books stacked in a pile on Lewis Carroll's bookshelf: *Alice's Adventures in Wonderland*; *Through the Looking-Glass, and What Alice Found There*; *Phantasmagoria and Other Poems*; and *The Hunting of the Snark*. One of these books was published in 1865, one in 1869, one in 1871, and one in 1876. The following is also true:

- *Through the Looking-Glass* is touching the book that was published in 1876.
- The book published in 1865 is higher in the stack than *Phantasmagoria and Other Poems*.
- The book at the bottom of the stack has the same number of words in its full title as the book published in 1865.
- The book published in 1869 is earlier in the alphabet than the book at the top of the stack.
- *Phantasmagoria and Other Poems* is not touching the book published in 1876.
- *The Hunting of the Snark* has at least one book above it.

Based on this information, can you deduce when each book was published and where it is in the stack? (In this puzzle it is important to note that the leading word *The* is ignored in establishing the alphabetical order of the titles.)

Labyrinth 1 ❧

Can you help Alice find her way through the circular labyrinth, avoiding all of the dead ends along the way?

Mathematical Mushroom 2

Can you fill the boxes in this mathematical mushroom with numbers from the range 1 to 9? Each connected number adds together to make the total given at the end of that line, and no number can be repeated within a line.

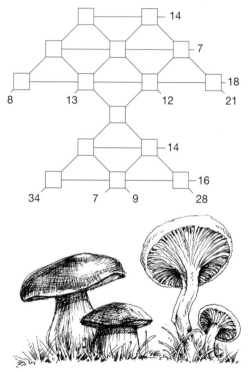

Guessing the Hand 1 ❧

Tweedledum is holding three cards:

- There is a jack to the left of a queen.
- There's a queen to the right of a club.
- There's a diamond to the left of a club.
- There's a diamond next to a queen.
- There's a diamond on the far right.

What are his cards?

Rebus 3 🐦

Can you identify the Carrollian word clued by the following?

LI CE

W

DERL&

Seating Arrangements

There are five people attending a Tea Party: the Hatter, the March Hare, the Dormouse, Alice, and the White Rabbit. There are also five seats in a row along a bench, and so they all move to sit down, but the Hatter stops them.

"Wait!" he says. "There's a seating plan!"

"Well, then, where you do want us to sit?" the White Rabbit asked anxiously.

"Hmm…" said the Hatter. "Well, I remember that the Dormouse isn't next to Alice or me. Alice isn't next to the March Hare, and neither is the White Rabbit. The White Rabbit isn't next to me, the March Hare is next to me on my right, and Alice is somewhere to the left of the White Rabbit."

Can you deduce where they should all sit in relation to one other?

Mathematical Mushroom 3 🍂

Can you fill the boxes in this mathematical mushroom with numbers from the range 1 to 9? Each connected number adds together to make the total given at the end of that line, and no number can be repeated within a line.

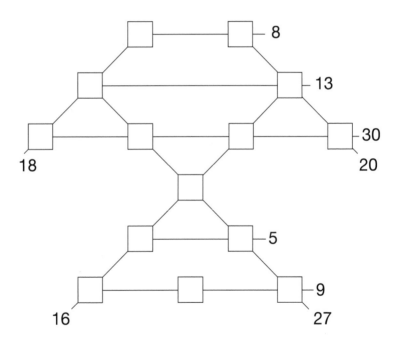

Rebus 4

Can you identify the Carrollian phrase clued by the following?

T

H

E

RABBIT

Guessing the Hand 2 ∾

Tweedledee is holding four cards:

- Reading them from left to right, the sum of the first three equals the fourth.
- Two cards have the same value, and are not adjacent.
- Two cards have the same suit, and are not adjacent.
- There's a heart to the left of a two.
- There's a three to the right of a heart.
- There's a spade to the right of a diamond.
- There's a heart next to a two.
- The farthest-left card is even.

What are his cards?

Wonderland Word Catalogue

The following words all have a Wonderland-related word in common. Can you identify it?

- Alley
- Burglar
- Fat
- Flap
- House
- Jungle

Mutual Words

Can you fill in each of the gaps below by finding a Wonderland-related word that can follow the first word in each pair and precede the second, making two two-word phrases in each case? Each phrase should be reasonably expected to be found in a dictionary.

FIELD ____ MAT

SPREAD ____ EYE

BEAUTY ____ BEE

SITTING ____ BOAT

NEST ____ TIMER

PRIMORDIAL ____ SPOON

Mixed Chapters 1 ∿

Can you unscramble these anagrammed chapter titles of *Alice's Adventures in Wonderland*? The length of each word in the chapter title is given.

If this is too tricky, solve the Split Titles puzzles on pages 64 and 70 to find the original titles.

- Coagulated casual enchanter. (3, 6, 4, 3, 1, 4, 4)

- Grotesque, conquered hunt. (3, 6, 7, 6)

- Littlest ideal babblers hint. (3, 6, 5, 1, 6, 4)

- The toothless wart. (3, 5, 3, 5)

Word Changer 1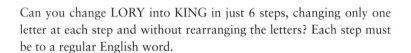

Can you change LORY into KING in just 6 steps, changing only one letter at each step and without rearranging the letters? Each step must be to a regular English word.

LORY

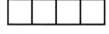

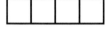

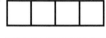

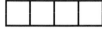

KING

For an extra challenge, can you find a way to change LORY into KING in just five steps, using an obscure word?

And then can you do it in four steps, with even more obscure words?

Mixed Chapters 2

Can you unscramble these anagrammed chapter titles of *Alice's Adventures in Wonderland*? The length of each word in the chapter title is given.

If this is too tricky, solve the Split Titles puzzles on pages 64 and 70 to find the original titles.

- Alive Decencies. (6, 8)

- Dapper pigpen. (3, 3, 6)

- Hot wobble in hatred. (4, 3, 6, 4)

- Loather of poets. (3, 4, 2, 5)

A Game for One 1 ∾

Alice came upon the following partially completed game, and felt that it would be quite wrong to continue without finishing it off.

She must place an X or an O into every empty square, so that *no* lines of four or more Xs or Os are made in any direction, including diagonally. How should she complete the game? (There is no requirement to use an equal number of Xs and Os.)

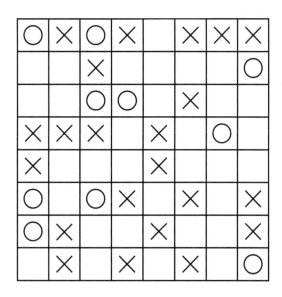

One Growing Potion ❧

In a cupboard of glasses in the Duchess's kitchen, Alice came across 1,000 bottles, each of which had a label sayin: Drink Me. She knew that exactly one of these bottles contained the growing potion she was looking for, while the rest would have no effect on her. A single sip of the growing potion would be enough to make her grow only slightly. She wanted to grow a lot, however, and since she didn't much like the taste of any of the potions, she wanted to find the bottle with the growing potion while drinking as little overall quantity of the potions as possible.

What is the fewest number of sips it would take her to identify the precise bottle which contains the growing potion?

Slaying the Jabberwock

Can you fill in the blanks in these lines from the poem "Jabberwocky" and then take the first letters in order from top to bottom and spell out a Wonderland-related word?

So rested he by the _____ tree

And the mome raths _____

And _____ in uffish thought he stood

_____ gyre and gimble in the wade

Twas brillig, and the _____ toves

Came whiffling through the _____ wood

One, two! _____, two! And through and through!

_____ frabjous day! Callooh! Callay!

_____ time the manxome foe he sought

Rearranging
Humpty Dumpty ❧

The poem "Humpty Dumpty" consists of 26 words. This means that each word of the poem can be assigned a different letter.

To decode the following quotation from the character Humpty Dumpty, you will need to assign each word of the poem a letter of the alphabet in order. So, starting with the first line, Humpty = A, Dumpty = B, sat = C, on = D, a = E, wall = F, and so on.

Now, using this assignment of words to letters, can you decode the following?

Put Dumpty a the/ had/ men the a/ Humpty/ put king's all on/ had king's/ all a Humpty the the/ a men the king's/ put Dumpty Humpty king's/ had/ all a Humpty the/ had king's/ king's king's/ all a Humpty the.

Note that some words will have multiple letters assigned to them (since those words repeat), so you'll have to use the context to work out which letter is meant.

174

Chessboard Assembly 1

Each square of a chessboard is identified by referring to its column letter, from A to H, and its row number, from 1 to 8. The first 5 rows and 5 columns of a particular chessboard have been cut up into separate squares, jumbled together, and then laid out again. Each square is marked with the original row and column it came from.

Given that no row or column contains two squares that have either the same number or the same letter, can you complete this chart showing where each original square has been placed?

B	C	4	E	D1
		5	C	
D4	1		A	C5
	4	C		
C2	5	D	1	4

Word Changer 2 🐦

Can you change LION into HARE in just 5 steps, changing only one letter at each step and without rearranging the letters? Each step must be to a regular English word, although the first step is to a relatively obscure literary word.

LION

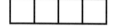

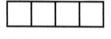

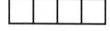

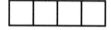

HARE

Labyrinth 2 🦋

Alice has been swept up by her pool of tears. Can you help her to find her way through from the top to the bottom of the labyrinth she has created?

Days and Days ❧

It was easy to lose track of time in Wonderland. Sometimes hours passed in minutes, and sometimes seconds took days.

"What day of the week is it?" Alice asked the Caterpillar one day.

"When the day after tomorrow is yesterday, then today will be as far from Monday as today was from Monday when the day before yesterday was tomorrow," said the Caterpillar.

So what day was it?

Eating at the Tea-Party

There was a big platter of cucumber sandwiches at the Tea Party.

The Hatter ate less than the Hare.

Tweedledum ate more than Tweedledee

Tweedledee ate more than the Hare, but less than the Dormouse.

Who ate the second-fewest sandwiches?

Alternate Letters 1 ☙

Can you identify the following Wonderland characters when only every other letter of their name is given?

_U E _ O _ H A T _

_H S _ E _ A _

_A C _ H R _

_W E _ L _ E

The Hole ❧

"How curious!" thought Alice one day, as she came upon a sudden hole in the road.

"Why, who would dig a hole in such a place? It is a most unremarkable spot to have chosen, and I can see no rhyme or reason as to its location.

"And yet it is an interesting hole, if holes can indeed be interesting (which I do think they can), for its sides are so perfectly cut into the surrounding soil.

"Indeed, I see that whoever who dug this hole was so proud of the hole that they have noted down its dimensions.

"Given that the hole claims to be 4 feet wide, 3 feet long, and 5 feet deep, what, I wonder, is the volume of the soil in this hole?"

Can you answer Alice's question?

Attacking Knights 1 ❧

Six different types of knight are to be placed onto a 6×6 board. Each type of knight is identified by a letter, from A to F.

Only one knight can be placed into any square, and some knights are already on the board. Can you replace the remaining knights so that every row and column contains one of each type of knight, A to F?

Also, knights must not be able to attack another knight of the same type in a single move. As in chess, this consists of moving one square horizontally and two squares vertically, or two squares horizontally and one square vertically. Therefore no two matching letters can be a single knight's move apart from one another.

Can you complete the board?

E		D	F		A
B					C
F					B
C		A	B		F

Wonderland Zigzag 2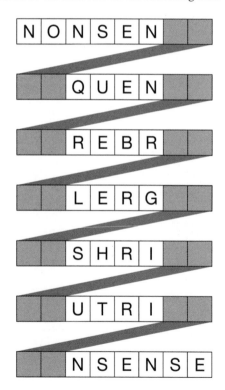

Can you fill in the gaps in the following zigzag puzzle, which starts and ends with a Wonderland-themed word? The last two letters of each word are the same as the first two of the following one.

| N | O | N | S | E | N | | |

| | | Q | U | E | N | | |

| | | R | E | B | R | | |

| | | L | E | R | G | | |

| | | S | H | R | I | | |

| | U | T | R | I | | | |

| | N | S | E | N | S | E | |

The Slow Climb ~

The White Rabbit was trying to climb back up out of a rabbit hole so as to leave Wonderland. The rabbit hole was 60 m high, and the Rabbit was able to climb up 6 m every ten minutes – but then his arms would give out and he'd sink back down 4 m again.

How long did it take him to climb the whole 60 m?

Alternate Letters 2 🍂

Can you identify the following Wonderland characters when only every other letter of their name is given?

_H_T_ R_B_I_

_O_K _U_T_E

_W_E_L_D_M

_U_P_Y _U_P_Y

Rebus 5 ❧

Can you identify the Wonderland resident clued by the following?

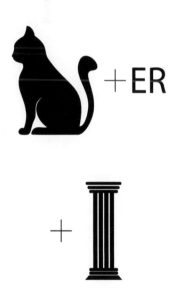

A Game for One 2 🐌

Alice came upon the following partially completed game, and felt that it would be quite wrong to continue without finishing it off.

She must place an X or an O into every empty square, so that *no* lines of four or more Xs or Os are made in any direction, including diagonally.

How should she complete the game? (There is no requirement to use an equal number of Xs and Os.)

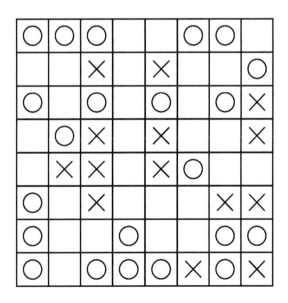

The Jackdaw's Puzzle ❧

Alice came presently upon a large dining table. She decided it must be a dining table, for it was set with all manner of knives, forks, spoons, and other cutlery items, some of which Alice was sure she had never seen before, and she could not begin to guess their use. There was not a morsel of food or drink on the table, which was rather a disappointment to Alice, who by this time was feeling rather hungry.

Alice was wondering whether to wait or carry on, when unexpectedly a jackdaw in a very small top hat appeared and spoke to Alice, saying, "Well, here's a pretty pickle. If you can help me with this teaser, I will have the table filled with food." Alice gladly signalled her desire to help, at which point the jackdaw continued: "My wife and I have been discussing this problem all day. She heard it from a raven, and he heard it from a crow, but you know how they are and the answer had been forgotten before the question had been solved. It's such a shame. I do hope you can help. The problem is rather simple, in fact, so I am sure you will be able to tell me what I imagine I already know."

This was rather a confusing statement, but to Alice's relief the actual problem was much simpler:

"In a far-off kingdom, boys and girls are equally likely to be born. But if the king then decrees that no couple can have any further children, once a boy is born to them, what effect will this have? In the future, will there be more girls than boys, or more boys than girls?"

How should Alice respond?

Word Changer 3 ~

Can you change ALICE into STORY in just 6 steps, changing only one letter at each step and without rearranging the letters? Each step must be to a regular English word.

ALICE

STORY

Labyrinth 3 🐌

Can you help Alice find her way across the croquet ground from top to bottom, avoiding all of the dead ends along the way?

Word Changer 4

Can you change SHEEP into FLOCK in just 6 steps, changing only one letter at each step and without rearranging the letters? Each step must be to a regular English word.

SHEEP

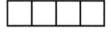

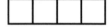

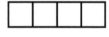

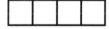

FLOCK

Attacking Knights 2 🐦

Seven different types of knight are to be placed onto a 7×7 board. Each type of knight is identified by a letter, from A to G.

Only one knight can be placed into any square, and some knights are already on the board. Can you replace the remaining knights so that every row and column contains one of each type of knight, A to G?

Also, knights must not be able to attack another knight of the same type in a single move. As in chess, this consists of moving one square horizontally and two squares vertically, or two squares horizontally and one square vertically. Therefore no two matching letters can be a single knight's move apart from one another.

Can you complete the board?

C						E
D						
	E			B		
		A			C	
						G
G						F

Mathematical Mushroom 4 🍂

Can you fill the boxes in this mathematical mushroom with numbers from the range 1 to 9? Each connected number adds together to make the total given at the end of that line, and no number can be repeated within a line.

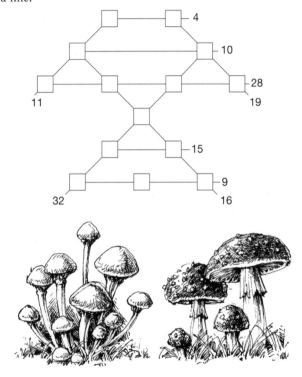

Rebus 6

Can you identify the Wonderland resident clued by the following rebus?

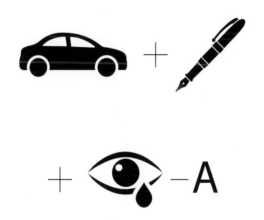

Labyrinth 4 🐾

The Cheshire Cat hasn't given Alice very helpful directions. Can you help her find her way through the forest of sloping trees? She is currently at the top of the forest, and needs to make her way to the bottom.

Gaps in the Looking-Glass ❧

Can you fill in each of the blanks in these *Through the Looking-Glass* chapter titles with one of the words from the righthand column?

Looking-Glass _____   Alice

The Garden of Live _____   Flowers

Tweedledum and _____   House

_____ and Water   Invention

The _____ and the Unicorn   It

"It's my own _____"   Lion

Queen _____   Tweedledee

Which dreamed _____?   Wool

Word Changer 5 ❧

Can you change HEART into SUITS in just 6 steps, changing only one letter at each step and without rearranging the letters? Each step must be to a regular English word.

HEART

SUITS

Labyrinth 5 🍂

Alice comes upon a curious pentagonal labyrinth, which she is determined to explore. Can you help her find her way through, all the way from left to right?

Rebus 7

Can you identify the Wonderland resident clued by the following?

Mixed Chapters 3

Can you unscramble these anagrammed chapter titles of *Alice's Adventures in Wonderland*? The length of each word in the chapter title is given.

If this is too tricky, solve the Split Titles puzzles on pages 64 and 70 to find the original titles.

- Adapt tame ray. (1, 3, 3-5)
- Farcical, pivotal dreamer. (6, 4, 1, 11)
- Idle quarrels blot. (7, 9)
- Mocker stutters hotly. (3, 4, 7, 5)

Chessboard Assembly 2 ↘

Each square of a chessboard is identified by referring to its column letter, from A to H, and its row number, from 1 to 8. The first 5 rows and 5 columns of a particular chessboard have been cut up into separate squares, jumbled together, and then laid out again. Each square is marked with the original row and column it came from.

Given that no row or column contains two squares that have either the same number or the same letter, can you complete this chart showing where each original square has been placed?

2	5	E	1	3
	E	2	D3	C4
C1	A3	D	4	
E	D	1	C	A

A Game for One 3 ❧

Alice came upon the following partially completed game, and felt that it would be quite wrong to continue without finishing it off.

She must place an X or an O into every empty square, so that *no* lines of four or more Xs or Os are made in any direction, including diagonally. How should she complete the game? (There is no requirement to use an equal number of Xs and Os.)

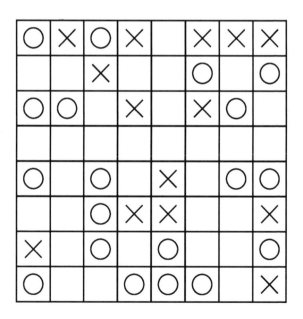

Chessboard Assembly 3 ~

Each square of a chessboard is identified by referring to its column letter, from A to H, and its row number, from 1 to 8. The first 5 rows and 5 columns of a particular chessboard have been cut up into separate squares, jumbled together, and then laid out again. Each square is marked with the original row and column it came from.

Given that no row or column contains two squares that have either the same number or the same letter, can you complete this chart showing where each original square has been placed?

1 C	B	4 E
2 E4	5	3
E		2
D	E	B5 C
4 A	3	2 D

Rebus 8 ❧

Can you identify the Wonderland resident clued by the following rebus?

Attacking Knights 3 ✎

Eight different types of knight are to be placed onto a 8×8 board. Each type of knight is identified by a letter, from A to H.

Only one knight can be placed into any square, and some knights are already on the board. Can you replace the remaining knights so that every row and column contains one of each type of knight, A to H?

Also, knights must not be able to attack another knight of the same type in a single move. As in chess, this consists of moving one square horizontally and two squares vertically, or two squares horizontally and one square vertically. Therefore no two matching letters can be a single knight's move apart from one another.

Can you complete the board?

B	F					H	C
H			E	D			F
		A			C		
	D					C	
	C					A	
		F			D		
A			G	C			E
D	A					E	B

Solutions

Time for Wonderland .... page 8

Twelve minutes past eleven.

Down the Rabbit Hole .... page 10

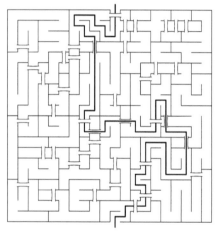

The Long Fall .... page 12

He had fallen off one of the lowest rungs of the ladder.

The Shrinking Bottle .... page 13

Alice would need to take six more sips after the original two. At this point she would be approximately 4.68 cm tall, and thus able to fit through the doorway.

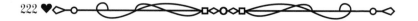

Solutions

Tweedledum and Tweedledee 1 . . . . page 14

Tweedledee. You know that at least one of them is lying about their name. Since they give different names, it cannot be the case that one of them is lying and the other is telling the truth for they would either both be called Tweedledum or both be called Tweedledee. So they must both be lying. Therefore, the one on the left must be Tweedledee, as he claims to be Tweedledum.

Too Big for Court . . . . page 17

She was 60 feet tall.

Remembering Forward . . . . page 18

Alice could easily *predict* the future. The hard part is predicting it *correctly*; she might well be wrong.

Not Enough Tea . . . . page 20

Alice simply needs to pour the tea from the first and third cups into the sixth and eighth cups.

Not Enough Cake . . . . page 22

Twenty-eight.

Three Bottles . . . . page 23

The mushroom potion was in the smallest bottle and would make her shrink. The carrot potion was in the medium-sized bottle and would make her grow. The pepper potion was in the biggest bottle and would not change her height at all.

Solutions

In The Kitchen . . . . page 24

One, if she takes a single vegetable from the basket marked POTATOES AND CARROTS. Whichever vegetable she removes from that basket, she can then deduce that all the vegetables in that basket are of that type. As the other two labels were also wrong, she could then deduce the contents of those too.

The Right Size . . . . page 26

Twelve: five bites of the cake and seven sips of the potion.

The Head Start . . . . page 28

The March Hare would win again. The first race demonstrated that he could run 100 m in the time it took the Hatter to run 90 m. So if they ran at the same speeds in the second race, they would draw level 10 m from the end. The Hare would then run the final 10 m more quickly than the Hatter, given that he was the faster runner.

The Not Lemonade . . . . page 30

Whatever it was that made Alice shrink must have been in the ice. The Cook drank her lemonade quickly, so the ice did not melt and she didn't ingest any of the shrinking substance. However, because Alice took much longer with hers, some of the ice melted while she drank and she ingested the substance that was in the ice.

Cake Selection . . . . page 31

Three: one carrot cake, one jam sponge, and one coffee cake.

Solutions

The Sentence . . . . page 32

The Bandersnatch was his best option. If the Bandersnatch hadn't eaten in two months, it was probably either dead or very weak!

Tweedledum and Tweedledee 2 . . . . page 34

Yes. The sentence *If I am Tweedledum, then my brother is Tweedledee* is false only if the speaker is Tweedledum and his brother is not Tweedledee. If the speaker were Tweedledee, then the sentence would be true, and Tweedledee cannot utter a true sentence, so the speaker cannot be Tweedledee and must be Tweedledum.

Too Many Queens . . . . page 36

Eight. There are only eight rows/columns on a chessboard, so we know the solution can't be more than eight. However, there are several ways to place eight queens so that they can't attack each other. For example:

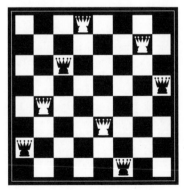

Solutions

Shifting Words 1 . . . . page 38

Shift each letter five places backward in the alphabet, so A becomes V, B becomes W, C becomes X, and so on, to read: *Why is a raven like a writing-desk?*

Tea Party Invitations . . . . page 39

The names were anagrams of:
- Cheshire Cat
- Queen of Hearts
- White Rabbit
- Knave of Hearts
- Mock Turtle

Down the Stairs . . . . page 40

There must have been a minimum of eight steps in the staircase.

Magic Mushrooms . . . . page 41

Alice's best bet is to take a mushroom from the basket marked Two for Shrinking. This basket either contains two mushrooms for growing, or one for growing and one for shrinking, meaning she has a ¾ chance of getting a growing mushroom. Using similar logic, the Two for Growing basket gives her only a ¼ chance of getting a growing mushroom, while the One for Growing and One for Shrinking basket either has two for growing or two for shrinking, so her chances of getting a growing mushroom from this basket are ½.

Solutions

A Pie Problem . . . . page 42

Alice put four pies each into the two smallest boxes and then put each of the two smallest boxes into one of the two biggest boxes. That way, each box contained exactly four pies.

The Hand that was Dealt . . . . page 44

The Dormouse held the two of hearts, the Hatter held the seven of diamonds, and the Hare held the queen of clubs.

Shifting Words 2 . . . . page 46

Shift each letter two places forward in the alphabet, so A becomes C, B becomes D, C becomes E, and so on, to read: *If you don't know where you are going, any road can take you there.*

Tweedledum and Tweedledee 3 . . . . page 47

He sometimes lies. If he always lied, then both brothers' statements would be true. So that statement must be false, and therefore the other is true.

Strange Sequences 1 . . . . page 48

These are the last letters of months of the year from January to July. The next month is August, so the next letter is T.

The Three Pieces . . . . page 50

The bishop was in E3, the pawn was in A7, and the rook was in B4.

Solutions

Looking Through the Looking Glass .... page 51

Since the books were themselves through the looking glass, their titles were written backward, and their letters differently spaced and punctuated. The books in English are:

- *To Kill A Mockingbird*, by Harper Lee
- *The Catcher in the Rye*, by J.D. Salinger
- *Finnegan's Wake*, by James Joyce
- *Alice's Adventures in Wonderland*, by Lewis Carroll

Strange Sequences 2 .... page 52

These are the first letters of days of the week from Wednesday to Monday. The next day is Tuesday, so the next letter is T.

Shifting Words 3 .... page 53

Shift each letter eight places backward in the alphabet, so A becomes S, B becomes T, C becomes U, and so on, to read: *I knew who I was this morning, but I've changed a few times since then.*

Hidden Figures .... page 54

- Alice: It was during the origin*al ice* age.
- Dodo: Taekwon*do do*esn't require much equipment.
- Gryphon: I made an an*gry phon*e call.
- Walrus: The plan for rene*wal rus*hed us.
- Hatter: I found t*hat ter*rifying.

Solutions

Character Match-up .... page 56

CHESHIRE	CAT
HUMPTY	DUMPTY
FROG	FOOTMAN
JUBJUB	BIRD
MAD	HATTER
MARCH	HARE
MOCK	TURTLE
RED	KING
WHITE	RABBIT

Too Many Legs .... page 58
There were 6 mice and 20 birds.

Stolen Vowels 1 .... page 60

CATERPILLAR
DORMOUSE
MAD HATTER
RED KING
WHITE RABBIT

Strange Sequences 3 .... page 62
These are the last letters of the sections of a rainbow, from red to indigo. The next is violet, so the next letter is T.

Strange Sequences 4 .... page 63
These are the first letters of elements of the periodic table, from hydrogen to oxygen. The next element is fluorine, so the next letter is F.

Solutions

Stolen Vowels 2 .... page 64

BANDERSNATCH
CHESHIRE CAT
MOCK TURTLE
MARCH HARE
TWEEDLEDUM

Split Titles 1 .... page 66

A_A_T_A_A_T_	_M_D_E_P_R_Y	A MAD TEA-PARTY
A_V_C_F_O_A_A_E_P_L_A_	_D_I_E_R_M_C_T_R_I_L_R	ADVICE FROM A CATERPILLAR
L_B_T_R_U_D_I_L_	_O_S_E_Q_A_R_L_E	LOBSTER QUADRILLE
T_E_A_B_T_E_D_A_I_T_E_I_L	_H_R_B_I_S_N_S_L_T_L_B_L_	THE RABBIT SENDS A LITTLE BILL
T_E_O_K_U_T_E_S_O_Y	_H_M_C_T_R_L_S_T_R_	THE MOCK TURTLE'S STORY
T_E_U_E_S_R_Q_E_G_O_N_	_H_Q_E_N_C_O_U_T_R_U_D	THE QUEEN'S CROQUET GROUND

Wonderful Words .... page 68

The pairs are: A + Lice, Cater + Pillar, Foot + Man, He + Arts, Hook + Ah, Mush + Room, Wonder + Land, and Uni + Corn. "Do" is the odd one out, as it can be paired with itself to make *dodo*.

Split Titles 2 .... page 70

A_I_E_E_I_E_C_	_L_C_S_V_D_N_E	ALICE'S EVIDENCE
D_W_T_E_A_B_T_O_E	_O_N_H_R_B_I_H_L_	DOWN THE RABBIT HOLE
P_G_N_P_P_E_	_I_A_D_E_P_R	PIG AND PEPPER
T_E_A_C_S_A_E_N_A_O_G_A_E	_H_C_U_U_R_C_A_D_L_N_T_L	THE CAUCUS RACE AND A LONG TALE
T_E_O_L_F_E_R_	_H_P_O_O_T_A_S	THE POOL OF TEARS
W_O_T_L_T_E_A_T_	_H_S_O_E_H_T_R_S	WHO STOLE THE TARTS?

Solutions

Strange Sequences 5 . . . . page 72
These are the first letters of whole numbers from one to seven. The next number is eight, so the next letter is E.

Tweedledum and Tweedledee 4 . . . . page 74
The jam sponges are the best, then the currant cakes, and then the chocolate cakes. Start by assuming that the second brother is telling the truth, and the chocolate cakes are not the worst. If this is true, then the first brother's statement is also true, because at least one half of the either/or claim is true, which is enough to make the claim as a whole true. As both brothers cannot be telling the truth, this means the second brother's claim must be false, and the chocolate cakes are the worst. In order for the first brother's claim to be true, it must be the case that the other half of his either/or claim is true: the jam sponges are the best. The currant cakes, which can be neither best nor worst, must be in the middle.

An Abundance of Tea . . . . page 75
He would pour his 150th cup on the 17th day of the exercise.

In Other Words . . . . page 76
The characters are:
- The Mad Hatter (loopy = mad, milliner = hatter)
- The March Hare (parade = march, leveret = hare)
- The Mock Turtle (ridicule = mock, reptile = turtle)
- The Unicorn (college = Uni, cereal seeds = corn)
- The Caterpillar (feline = cat, um = er, column = pillar)

Solutions

Changing Sizes .... page 78

She ate the cake in the morning and it made her 300 cm tall. She drank the potion in the afternoon and it made her 50 cm tall. She ate the mushroom in the evening and it made her 150 cm tall.

The Wrong Names .... page 80

Zero. If she was right about fourteen names, then she would also have to be right about the fifteenth.

Birds of a Feather .... page 82

26.

A Sponge Shared .... page 84

It would take Tweedledee an hour to eat the cake on his own. If it takes Tweedledum 30 minutes to eat the whole cake, then in ⅔ of the time – 20 minutes – he must eat ⅔ of the cake. This means that in 20 minutes Tweedledee eats ⅓ of the cake, so it would take him three times that to eat the whole cake.

Madness and Nonsense .... page 86

The Cheshire Cat could be right. If 30 per cent of Wonderland residents were a lot madder than the rest, then they could drag up the average so that the other 70 per cent were less mad than average. This works so long as the average is defined as the mean, as it usually is unless otherwise specified, and if madness can indeed be quantified.

Solutions

Shifting Words 4 .... page 88

Shift each letter eleven places forward in the alphabet, so A becomes L, B becomes M, C becomes N, and so on, to read: *Why, sometimes I've believed as many as six impossible things before breakfast.*

Too Big for the Kitchen .... page 90

12.16.

Before the Trial .... page 92

Thirteen.

Collecting Mushrooms .... page 93

No. If half the mushrooms have already taken her twice as long as they should have taken, then she's already out of time.

Tweedledum and Tweedledee 5 .... page 94

She could ask one of the brothers a question along the lines of: *If I asked your brother whether that was the way to the Royal Garden, would he say yes?* If it was the right way, then the lying brother would lie about the honest brother's answer and answer "no", and the honest brother would tell the truth about the honest brother's answer and also answer "no." If it was the wrong way, they would both say "yes" for the same reasons.

Plates of Cakes .... page 96

Twelve. There would need to be 91 cakes to make it to thirteen plates.

Solutions

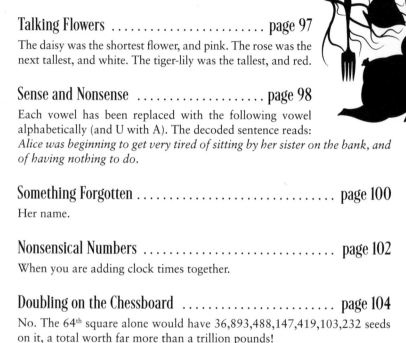

Talking Flowers .... page 97

The daisy was the shortest flower, and pink. The rose was the next tallest, and white. The tiger-lily was the tallest, and red.

Sense and Nonsense .... page 98

Each vowel has been replaced with the following vowel alphabetically (and U with A). The decoded sentence reads:
Alice was beginning to get very tired of sitting by her sister on the bank, and of having nothing to do.

Something Forgotten .... page 100

Her name.

Nonsensical Numbers .... page 102

When you are adding clock times together.

Doubling on the Chessboard .... page 104

No. The 64th square alone would have 36,893,488,147,419,103,232 seeds on it, a total worth far more than a trillion pounds!

Too Many Bishops .... page 106

Thirteen. There are fifteen diagonals on a chessboard going from top left to bottom right, so there couldn't be more than fifteen bishops that didn't share a diagonal (and in fact, you could not fit more than fourteen because the first and last diagonal would share a perpendicular diagonal line). In

Solutions

addition, in a corner of the board (where there is a diagonal of one that touches both squares of its adjacent diagonals of two), there can only be one bishop in total in those two diagonals, otherwise they'd be adjacent. This is true for both the top right corner and the bottom left corner (given that we are considering diagonals from top left to bottom right), bringing the maximum down to thirteen.

The Dinner Conundrum . . . . page 107

Alice, for the organizer of the tea had replaced "lice" with a synonym, "nits." The nameplate could thus be read as "A lice," or "Alice."

More Sense and Nonsense . . . . page 108

Every other letter has been replaced with the previous letter alphabetically (and A with Z). The decoded sentence reads: *One thing was certain, that the white kitten had had nothing to do with it—it was the black kitten's fault entirely.*

Tweedledum and Tweedledee 6 . . . . page 110

Yes. The sentence *You may borrow the boat if and only if my name is Tweedledum* results in the following possibilities:
a) Alice may borrow the boat and the speaker is Tweedledum; *or*
b) Alice may not borrow the boat and the speaker is not Tweedledum.
If the speaker was indeed Tweedledum, his sentence was true, so either a) or b) must be the case. Moreover, as his name is Tweedledum, b) can't be true and so a) must be true, and Alice may borrow the boat.
Alternatively, if the speaker was Tweedledee, his sentence was false, and neither a) nor b) is true. Moreover, as his name is not Tweedledum, then it cannot be the case that Alice may not borrow the boat, or else b) would be true. So, Alice may borrow the boat.

Solutions

Mathematical Mushroom 1 .... page 112

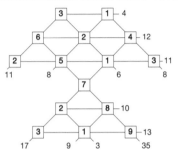

Back to Square One .... page 114

There are 204 squares: 64 that are 1×1, 49 that are 2×2, 36 that are 3×3, 25 that are 4×4, 16 that are 5×5, 9 that are 6×6, 4 that are 7×7, and one that is 8×8.

Broken Chessboard .... page 116

Solutions

Chess and Dominoes .... page 118

No, it's not possible. Opposite corners of a chessboard are the same (both black or both white), so by cutting them off Tweedledee was left with either more black squares or more white squares. But each domino will cover exactly one white square and one black square, as no two white or black squares are adjacent. So after placing 30 dominoes, there will inevitably be two squares left, both either white or black. These will not be adjacent and so cannot be covered by a single domino.

Shifting Words 5 .... page 119

Shift each letter six places backward in the alphabet, so A becomes U, B becomes V, C becomes W, and so on, to read: *Imagination is the only weapon in the war against reality.*

Card Tricks .... page 120

The cards he gave to Alice were, apart from the three of diamonds, the only cards that are not rotationally symmetrical. If any of these had been rotated, he would have been able to see the rotation. But, because nothing had changed, he knew she must have rotated the only rotationally symmetrical card in the stack, the three of diamonds.

Card Watching .... page 122

42. There are four eyes on each of the four queen cards. There are four eyes on the kings of clubs, spades, and hearts, but the king of diamonds has only one eye on each face. There are four eyes on the jacks of diamonds and clubs, but the jacks of spades and hearts have only one eye on each face.

Solutions

House of Cards . . . . page 124

9 layers. The bottom layer would have 10 cards in, then 4 flat cards, then 8 upright cards, then 3 flat cards, then 6 upright cards, then 2 flat, then 4 upright, then 1 flat, then 2 at the top, using 40 cards in total. This leaves only 12 cards, which is not enough for both a flat layer of 5 and an upright layer of 12 to be added beneath.

Blind Man's Bluff . . . . page 126

He sorted the cards into one pile of 16 and one pile of 36. He then flipped all the cards in the pile of 16.

Four of a Kind . . . . page 127

40. The answer is the same for one pack or for many. If you had 39 cards, you could have three of a kind of each value, but no four of a kind. The next card you drew would have to be the same value as one of the threes, making four of a kind.

Even More Sense and Nonsense . . . . page 128

Each letter has been swapped with its opposite in the alphabet, so A with Z, B with Y, C with X, and so on. The decoded passage reads: *Now, here, you see, it takes all the running you can do, to keep in the same place. If you want to get somewhere else, you must run at least twice as fast as that!*

Solutions

Rebus 1 . . . . page 130

Six impossible things before breakfast: 6 × not "possible" before "things" before the broken "fast."

Mad Multiplication . . . . page 131

Zero. Many (and at least one) of the residents of Wonderland do not have hands, and multiplying any number by zero gives zero as the answer.

Wonderland Zigzag 1 . . . . page 132

C	H	E	S	H	I	R	E

R	E	N	E	G	A	D	E

D	E	C	R	E	A	S	E

S	E	Q	U	O	I	A	S

A	S	S	A	S	S	I	N

I	N	N	U	E	N	D	O

D	O	R	M	O	U	S	E

Solutions

Nonsense Pairs . . . . page 134

- Queen of Hearts
- Mad Hatter
- Alice
- March Hare
- Tweedledee

Letter Soup . . . . page 136

The names are Alice, Tweedledum, and Duchess.

Muddled Testimonies . . . . page 138

Bill the Lizard saw the Knave of Hearts sleeping in the Duchess' kitchen at 9 a.m. The White Rabbit saw him reading a book in the royal gardens at 2 p.m. The March Hare saw him eating the tarts beneath a giant mushroom at 7 p.m.

The Road to the Palace . . . . page 140

Only Alice: the others were all going in the opposite direction.

The Giant Puppy . . . . page 142

Halfway. After that, you're leaving the woods again.

Rebus 2 . . . . page 144

Through the looking-glass: "LOOK" in "G-GLASS" through "THE."

Solutions

A Slow Race .... page 146

She suggested that they swap trousers, or take a piece of each other's trousers. This would mean that whoever got there first could touch the other's trousers to the seat and thus win.

Lewis Carroll's Bookshelf .... page 148

Alice's Adventures in Wonderland was published in 1865 and is third from the top of the stack. *Through the Looking-Glass, and What Alice Found There* was published in 1871 and is at the top of the stack. *Phantasmagoria and Other Poems* was published in 1869 and is at the bottom of the stack. *The Hunting of the Snark* was published in 1876 and is second from the top of the stack.

Labyrinth 1 .... page 149

Solutions

Mathematical Mushroom 2 . . . . page 150

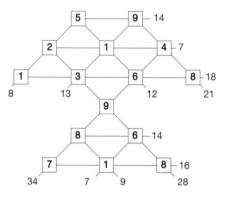

Guessing the Hand 1 . . . . page 151

He has (from left to right) a jack of diamonds, a queen of clubs, and a queen of diamonds.

Rebus 3 . . . . page 152

Alice in Wonderland: A "LICE" in "W" on "DERL" and an "and."

Seating Arrangements . . . . page 154

From left to right, they should sit in the following order: Alice, the Hatter, the March Hare, the Dormouse, and then the White Rabbit.

Solutions

Mathematical Mushroom 3 . . . . page 156

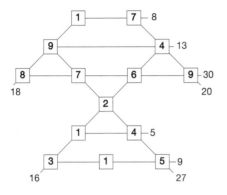

Rebus 4 . . . . page 158

Down the rabbit hole: "THE" going down, and a hole in "RABBIT."

Guessing the Hand 2 . . . . page 159

He has (from left to right) a two of hearts, a three of diamonds, a two of spades, and a seven of hearts.

Wonderland Word Catalogue . . . . page 160

The common word is *cat*. Each word on the list can be either preceded or followed by *cat* to make a dictionary entry: alley cat, cat burglar, fat cat, cat flap, house cat, and jungle cat.

Solutions

Mutual Words .... page 162

The phrases are: mouse (*field mouse* and *mouse mat*), eagle (*spread eagle* and *eagle eye*), queen (*beauty queen* and *queen bee*), duck (*sitting duck* and *duck boat*), egg (*nest egg* and *egg timer*) and soup (*primordial soup* and *soup spoon*).

Mixed Chapters 1 .... page 164

- The Caucus Race and a Long Tale
- The Queen's Croquet Ground
- The Rabbit Sends a Little Bill
- Who Stole the Tarts?

Word Changer 1 .... page 166

LORY LORD FORD FOND FIND KIND KING
Five steps: LORY LORE LONE LINE KINE KING
Four steps: LORY LIRY LINY LING KING

Mixed Chapters 2 .... page 168

- Alice's Evidence
- Pig and Pepper
- Down the Rabbit Hole
- The Pool of Tears

Solutions

A Game for One 1 .... page 170

◯	✕	◯	✕	◯	✕	✕	✕
◯	✕	✕	✕	◯	✕	◯	◯
✕	◯	◯	◯	✕	✕	✕	◯
✕	✕	✕	◯	✕	◯	◯	◯
✕	◯	◯	◯	✕	✕	◯	✕
◯	✕	◯	✕	◯	✕	◯	✕
◯	✕	◯	✕	✕	◯	✕	✕
◯	✕	✕	✕	◯	✕	✕	◯

One Growing Potion .... page 171

She need only take a maximum of ten sips. She could do this by putting a drop from each of 500 of the bottles in a glass and taking a sip. If this had an effect, she could discard the other 500. If not, she could discard the 500 that the sip had come from. She could then do the same by combining 250 bottles from the 500 she had left, and so on with 125 bottles, 63 bottles, 32 bottles, 16 bottles, 8 bottles, 4 bottles, 2 bottles and finally 1 bottle. When she drank that final bottle, if it had an effect, she would have found her potion – and if not, it was the other remaining bottle. This makes a total of 10 sips to identify the exact bottle.

Solutions

Slaying the Jabberwock .... page 172

The poem with the missing words reinserted is:

So rested he by the **Tumtum** tree
And the mome raths **outgrabe**
And **as** in uffish thought he stood
Did gyre and gimble in the wade
Twas brillig, and the **slithy** toves
Came whiffling through the **tulgey** wood
One, two! **One**, two! And through and through!
O frabjous day! Callooh! Callay!
Long time the manxome foe he sought

So the word the first letters spell out is TOADSTOOL.

Rearranging Humpty Dumpty .... page 174

The full poem is:
Humpty (A) Dumpty (B) sat (C) on (D) a (E) wall (F)
Humpty (G) Dumpty (H) had (I) a (J) great (K) fall (L)
All (M) the (N) king's (O) horses (P) and (Q) all (R) the (S) king's (T) men (U)
Couldn't (V) put (W) Humpty (X) together (Y) again (Z)
The decoded quotation is therefore: *When I use a word it means just what I mean it to mean.*

Solutions

Chessboard Assembly 1 . . . . page 176

B5	C3	A4	E2	D1
A1	D2	E5	C4	B3
D4	E1	B2	A3	C5
E3	B4	C1	D5	A2
C2	A5	D3	B1	E4

Word Changer 2 . . . . page 178
LION LIMN LIME LIRE HIRE HARE

Labyrinth 2 . . . . page 180

Solutions

Days and Days .... page 182
Monday.

Eating at the Tea-Party .... page 183
The Hare.

Alternate Letters 1 .... page 184
QUEEN OF HEARTS
CHESHIRE CAT
MARCH HARE
TWEEDLEDEE

The Hole .... page 185
The volume of soil inside the hole is clearly zero, or otherwise it would not be such a perfectly cut hole.

Attacking Knights 1 .... page 186

E	C	D	F	B	A
A	B	F	E	C	D
B	F	E	A	D	C
F	E	C	D	A	B
D	A	B	C	F	E
C	D	A	B	E	F

Solutions

Wonderland Zigzag 2 . . . . page 188

N O N S E N S E

S E Q U E N C E

C E R E B R A L

A L L E R G E N

E N S H R I N E

N E U T R I N O

N O N S E N S E

The Slow Climb . . . . page 190

280 minutes. The White Rabbit was progressing at a rate of 2 m every ten minutes, so at the end of 270 minutes, he would have climbed 54 m. Therefore, at the end of the next ten minutes he would have reached the top by climbing the remaining 6 m, and it wouldn't matter that he would have slipped back down 4 m if he was still mid-climb.

Alternate Letters 2 . . . . page 192

WHITE RABBIT
MOCK TURTLE
TWEEDLEDUM
HUMPTY DUMPTY

Solutions

Rebus 5 .... page 193

Caterpillar: cat + er + pillar.

A Game for One 2 .... page 194

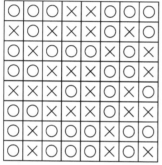

The Jackdaw's Puzzle .... page 196

The rule will have no effect on the likelihood of any child being born a boy or a girl, no matter what other rules are applied. The only difference will be that some couples are forbidden from having further children.

Word Changer 3 .... page 197

One possible solution is ALICE SLICE SLICK STICK STOCK STORK STORY

Solutions

Labyrinth 3 . . . . page 198

Word Changer 4 . . . . page 200

One possible solution is SHEEP CHEEP CHEEK CHECK CHOCK CLOCK
FLOCK

Attacking Knights 2 . . . . page 202

C	G	B	D	F	A	E
D	B	G	F	C	E	A
A	E	F	C	B	G	D
E	F	D	A	G	B	C
F	D	A	G	E	C	B
B	A	C	E	D	F	G
G	C	E	B	A	D	F

Solutions

Mathematical Mushroom 4 . . . . page 204

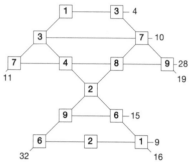

Rebus 6 . . . . page 205

The Carpenter: car + pen + (tear − a).

Labyrinth 4 . . . . page 206

Solutions

Gaps in the Looking-Glass .... page 208

Looking-Glass House
The Garden of Live Flowers
Tweedledum and Tweedledee
Wool and Water
The Lion and the Unicorn
"It's my own invention"
Queen Alice
Which dreamed it?

Word Changer 5 .... page 209

One possible solution is HEART HEARS HEATS SEATS SLATS SLITS SUITS

Labyrinth 5 .... page 210

Solutions

Rebus 7 . . . . page 211
Duchess: (Duck-ck) + chess

Mixed Chapters 3 . . . . page 212
A Mad Tea-Party
Advice from a Caterpillar
Lobster Quadrille
The Mock Turtle's Story

Chessboard Assembly 2 . . . . page 214

D2	C5	E4	A1	B3
B5	E1	A2	D3	C4
A4	B2	C3	E5	D1
C1	A3	D5	B4	E2
E3	D4	B1	C2	A5

Solutions

A Game for One 3 . . . . page 216

O	×	O	×	O	×	×	×
O	×	×	×	O	O	×	O
O	O	O	×	×	×	O	O
×	O	×	O	O	O	×	×
O	×	O	O	×	×	O	O
O	O	×	O	×	×	O	×
×	×	O	O	O	×	O	O
O	O	×	O	O	O	×	×

Chessboard Assembly 3 . . . . page 218

D1	C5	B2	A4	E3
C2	E4	A5	D3	B1
E5	B3	D4	C1	A2
A3	D2	E1	B5	C4
B4	A1	C3	E2	D5

Solutions

Rebus 8 . . . . page 219
Cheshire Cat: (chess – s) + h + (fire – f) + cat

Attacking Knights 3 . . . . page 220

B	F	E	D	A	G	H	C
H	G	C	E	D	A	B	F
G	H	A	B	E	C	F	D
F	D	B	A	G	E	C	H
E	C	D	F	H	B	A	G
C	E	F	H	B	D	G	A
A	B	H	G	C	F	D	E
D	A	G	C	F	H	E	B